Nest

by Mererid Hopwood

www.peniarth.cymru

Illustrated by Rhiannon Sparks.

Published in 2017 by Canolfan Peniarth.

Carew Castle present day

Our story begins in Carew Castle in Pembrokeshire. Today, it's in ruins.

But I wonder if you can imagine the castle as a brand new building?

Can you imagine the flags flying high in the wind and people busy at work there?

Some are cleaning, others cooking, some are keeping watch and some are sharpening their weapons. Yes, weapons! Because these were dangerous times in Wales, and people were all too ready to fight against one another.

The castle has been built by Gerald Fitzwalter, and he's very

pleased with it. Gerald Fitzwalter is sometimes known as Gerald de Windsor, and he's one of the Normans who wants to conquer Wales.

Sitting with her maid, Meinir, in one of the castle rooms is Princess Nest …

"So here I am. Nest, daughter of Rhys ap Tewdwr, King of the Deheubarth, King of all of South Wales."

Nest was looking at her reflection in the glass. Behind her stood Meinir, her maid. Meinir had been combing Nest's hair, and now she had started to tie it neatly.

Nest and Meinir were friends and would spend hours together. Though Nest liked to wear beautiful clothes, she hated having her hair tied back. She much preferred letting her hair flow freely down over her shoulders.

"Oh! Do you have to tie my hair back?" she complained to Meinir.

"Princess Nest!" answered Meinir, "You know that you're famous throughout the land for being such a beautiful princess! Your husband, Gerald de Windsor, says time and again that you must dress like a princess and live like a princess. You have no choice in the matter. We must make sure that your hair is neat and tidy. Every single strand must be in its place."

"Tut! Gerald indeed!" says Nest, impatiently.

Nest hadn't chosen to marry her husband. Henry I, King of England, had arranged for her to marry Gerald in the hope that the marriage would help the Welsh and the Normans

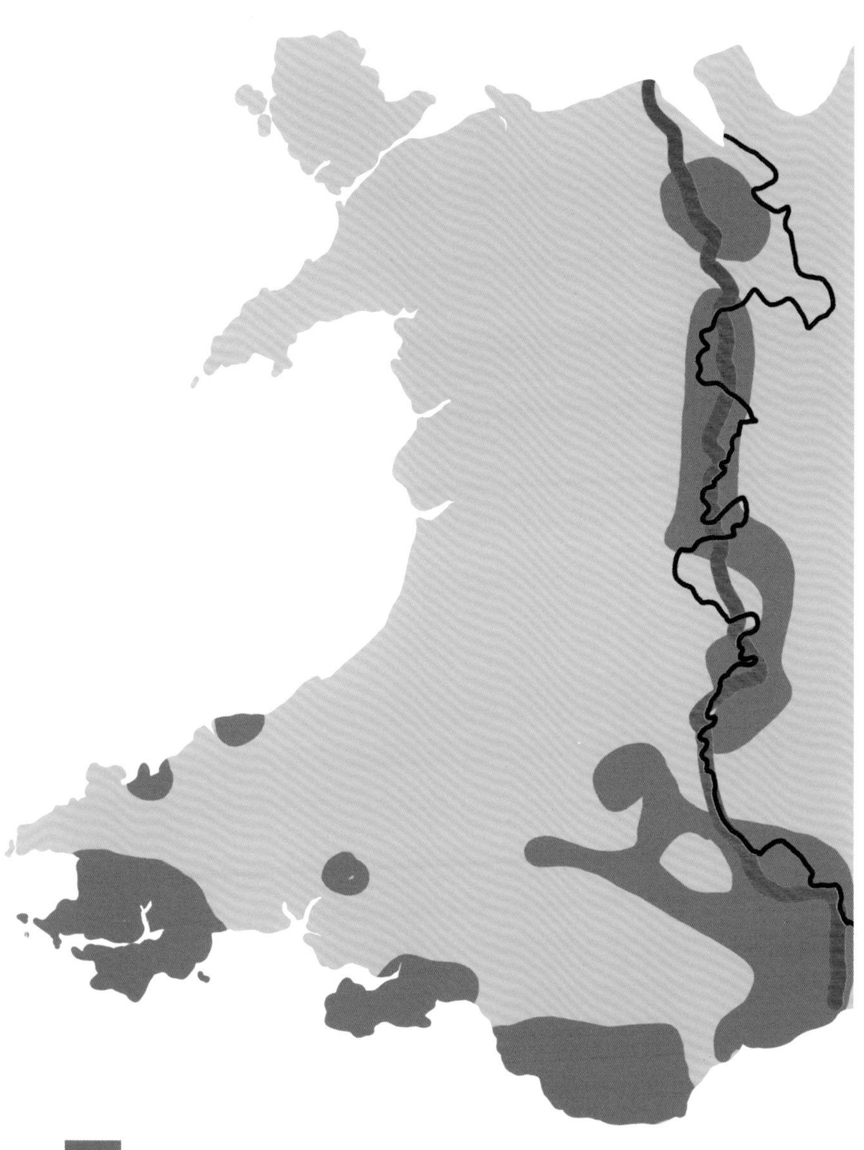

Norman rule

Offa's Dyke

Modern border

get along better. Though Nest seemed to lead quite a happy life with Gerald, sometimes she would be very cross about this arrangement, and if someone had asked Nest, she would have said that she thought Gerald preferred his castles to his family, and that he was more concerned about his land than his own wife!

As you already know, Nest lived in troubled times. The Normans had come to Britain in 1066 and had quickly conquered England. At first, they hadn't been able to make much inroad into Wales, but recently, they had started to advance West. They were determined to take land in Wales too.

Henry had hoped that a marriage between Nest, a Welsh princess, and Gerald de Windsor, one of the Normans, would persuade the Welsh to give up their fighting. But his plans hadn't worked and the fighting continued.

By now, Meinir had finished arranging Nest's hair. With eyes full of sadness, Nest turned to Meinir and held both her hands tightly, before saying:

"I'm afraid, Meinir! There was such a loud noise last night again. Soldiers were fighting. Did you hear the shouting?"

Meinir didn't say a word; she simply looked back at Nest. Meinir too looked sad. Nest knew full well that Meinir had heard the shouting. She knew that Meinir was afraid too.

Nest got up and ventured to the slit in the wall that let some light into the dark room. In a quiet voice she whispered:

"The castle walls shook and trembled!"

Then she ran back towards Meinir and asked: "Do you think we'll have to escape again?"

Without lifting her eyes, Meinir replied:

"Yes, Nest, we will leave Carew Castle before long. I have already packed everything, just in case."

Nest was fed up with all the moving. How many times had she and her family fled from castle to castle to castle?

Ever since her father was killed in the battle in Brecon in 1093, life had been difficult for Nest.

At night, lying awake in her bed, she would remember the time she was kidnapped by her father's enemies.

She remembered the loud noise in the castle. She remembered the footsteps thundering towards her room. She remembered how somebody had flung a sack over her head and dragged her out to take her to a secret destination.

She remembered trying to fight back and shouting for help.

And she remembered being locked in a strange castle.

She would try her best to forget the whole episode, but when night fell, forgetting was difficult. That's why she was so glad to have Meinir's company.

"They didn't let me out of that room for such a long time ..."

"Nest!" said Meinir. "That's enough! There's no point in revisiting that night all the time. Put it out of your mind!"

"But Meinir!" said Nest. "I thought I would never see my family again."

"There's no good in thinking horrid thoughts, Nest. It's almost Christmas. Let's think about that. Let's be merry!"

"You're quite right, Meinir. Horrid thoughts create more horrid thoughts."

In order to cheer Nest up, Meinir said:

"Do you remember living in Pembroke Castle? The views were so lovely from that castle. The children used to enjoy seeing the boats come down the River Cleddau and into Pembroke town."

"You're right," said Nest. "And then we had to leave Pembroke quickly to come here, to Carew Castle. That's all Gerald and the Normans seem to do - build castles! Carew Castle, Pembroke Castle, Cenarth Bychan Castle ... I'm sure there are more castles in Wales than in any other country in the whole wide world!"

"But this castle has been such a lovely home. And the stone tower is a wonder. Everybody in the land is amazed to see it," replied Meinir.

"Tut! A stone tower indeed!" said Nest. "No tower is strong enough to keep us safe. And tomorrow we will have to flee again. Just you wait. I heard that this time we must go to Cenarth Bychan Castle ... Castles! Castles! Castles!"

Nest turned again to look at Meinir and ask:

"Why can't the Welsh and the Normans just be friends? It's so hard to be the daughter of a Welshman and the wife of a Norman."

Meinir said nothing, but in her heart, she too had a question. Her question was: 'Why are the Normans trying to steal Welsh land?' Meinir didn't think that was fair at all.

After the sun had set that evening, everybody - Gerald de Windsor, Princess Nest, Meinir and all the children - fled to Cenarth Bychan Castle.

The children were warned not to utter a word. Not one single little syllable. They had to be as quiet as possible in order to avoid attracting attention.

It was bitterly cold and the night breeze bit their bones. Nest could see that all the stars in the sky were twinkling and, to keep the children still, Nest whispered to them a story about a beautiful girl called Olwen, who lived in a large hall in the Land of Stars. Wherever Olwen would go, a new star would be born just underneath her foot. When Olwen was happy, she would dance through the black night and wherever she danced, a hundred new baby stars would appear. On this cold December night, it was clear that Olwen had been dancing for ages.

Nest and Meinir had wrapped everybody in warm woollen blankets and, between Nest's story and Meinir's soft singing, the little children fell fast asleep.

Oh, how Nest hoped that the whole family would finally be safe and sound in Cenarth Bychan, far from the fearful fighting!

And so it was. When the children woke up in the morning, they were in their new home. This time, it was the River Teifi that they could see flowing by. The River Teifi was a lovely river and, from the castle, you could hear the cold water murmuring its way towards the mighty sea.

Shortly after they moved to Cenarth Bychan, a message came from Owain ap Cadwgan, Prince of Powys. Owain ap Cadwgan was a famous Welsh leader, and he sent word to Nest and Gerald telling them that he would like to call in to the castle to visit them. As Owain was related to Nest, everybody was very pleased to invite him and his friends to come and enjoy a feast in their company.

Nest was delighted! At last, something exciting. A feast!

Nest arranged the feast with the cook in the castle. They ordered all sorts of foods and asked the court poet and harpist to compose special songs to welcome Owain.

Unfortunately, Owain ap Cadwgan hadn't told them exactly why he wanted to come to the castle!

The truth of the matter was that Owain ap Cadwgan, like everybody in Wales, had heard of Nest's beauty. For many months, Owain had started to dream about her. He didn't want to meet Gerald de Windsor at all! His plan was to see Nest with his own eyes and take her from Gerald!

Everything was ready. The tables were creaking with fine foods and the castle was in splendid shape. Owain arrived with around fourteen of his men, and Gerald and Nest welcomed them warmly. The moment Owain saw Nest, he realised that what he had heard about her was true. Never before had he seen anybody as beautiful in all his life. He was determined to steal her from Gerald!

"Why should a Norman have such a beautiful Welsh wife?" raged Owain to himself.

Having eaten, they all sat by the enormous fire and listened to the poet's tales. Nest was so very happy.

At last, it was time to sleep, and one by one they all went to bed.

But Owain ap Cadwgan didn't have the slightest intention of sleeping …

He waited until the castle was completely quiet. Then, in the pitch black, Owain and his men climbed the castle walls towards Nest's chamber, and set the whole castle on fire.

What a panic! Everybody ran in all directions!

The servants, the soldiers, the dogs, the cats, the bats, the fox, the mice and all the castle family were screaming and screeching.

In the panic, Nest had an idea. In the far corner of her chamber there was a toilet with a large pipe that led all the way from the top of the castle outside to the bottom. Nest pushed her husband through the pipe and out of Owain's sight!

The toilet pipe was a bit smelly - but at least Gerald was safe!

Nest shouted at the soldiers: "Don't bother coming any closer, Gerald has escaped!"

But at that very moment, who came into the chamber but Owain himself! Without hesitation, Owain got hold of Nest and whipped her up in his arms and out of the castle into the black night and far, far away from Cenarth Bychan.

When Gerald de Windsor realised what had happened, he was furious!

You can imagine, I'm sure, how the fighting between the Normans and the Welsh became even fiercer. In the end, Owain had to flee for his life to Ireland. When he returned, he was kidnapped by Flemish soldiers under Gerald's command. These soldiers were expert archers and they killed Owain without mercy.

Nobody's sure when Gerald died, but Nest went to live with the Sheriff of Pembrokeshire, William Hait, before marrying Steffan, Constable of Ceredigion.

And nobody's quite sure when Nest died, but it was probably around the year 1136.

And some say that her spirit still walks through the ruins of Carew Castle to this day.

One thing that we know for sure is that Nest had a grandson called Gerallt. Gerallt grew to be a very important Welshman. He travelled through the whole country making notes and recording the history of Wales in a book called in Latin 'Itineriarum Cambriae', or in Welsh 'Taith drwy Gymru', which translates into English as 'The Journey through Wales'. Today, we know him as 'Gerallt Gymro' or 'Giraldus Cambrensis' or Gerald of Wales.

Just like his grandmother, Nest, he could speak Welsh and Norman, which was a language close to French, and his famous book was written in Latin. We can learn a great deal about Wales by reading Gerallt's book.

This book is part of the 'Travelling back to the Middle Ages' series, which includes …

ISBN 978-1-78390-099-2

Learners' travel guidebook

Story book

Picture cards

Teachers' book

Virtual tour

Famous Personalities

ISBN 978-1-78390-098-5

Learners' travel guidebook

Story book

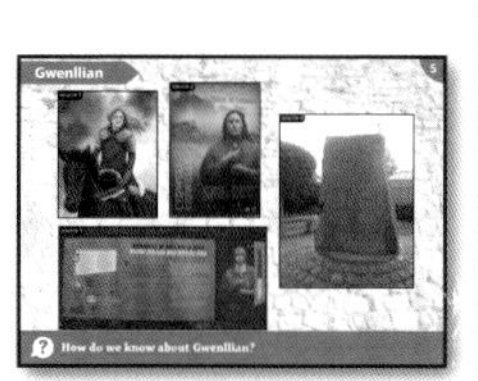

Picture cards

Teachers' book

Actor film clips